Another Animal Alphabet

Another Animal Alphabet

Richard Digance
With illustrations by Diana Gold

Michael Joseph . London

First published in Great Britain by
Michael Joseph Ltd
44 Bedford Square, London WC1
1982

ISBN 0 7181 2197 X

Photoset by Rowland Phototypesetting Ltd
Bury St Edmunds, Suffolk

Printed in Great Britain by
Fletcher & Son Ltd, Norwich

Contents

The Alligator   8

The Antelope   10

The Armadillo   11

The Badger   12

The Battery Hen   13

The Bear   15

The Boar   17

The Canary   17

The Cat   18

The Cheetah   20

The Cricket   20

The Dingo   21

The Dogfish   21

The Dolphin   23

The Donkey   24

The Earwig   24

The Eel   25

The Elk   25

The Elephants and the Great
    Bun-Fighting Contest   26

The Ferret   28

The Fly   29

The Fox   29

The Gibbon   30

The Giraffes and Gorillas Meet Again at the
    Second Jungle Cup Final   31

The Hedgehog   35
The Horse   35
The Hippo and the Insect   37
The Iguana   39
The Jaguar   39
The Jellyfish   39
The Kestrel   40
The Kingfisher   40
The Limpet   42
The Lion and the Sea Lion   43
The Lizard   44
The Mole   47
The Money Spider   48
The Monkey   49
The Letter N   49
The Nutria   50
The Octopus   50
The Ostrich   52
Amanda the Panda   53
The Pigeon   53
The Piranha   56
The Prairie Dog   56
The Quail   57
The Rabbit   58
The Reindeer   60
The Robin   63
The Skunk   64
The Slug   65
Two Snakes   65

The Squirrel   67
The Tiger (The Sabre-Toothless Tiger)   68
The Turbot   68
Mr Turtle   70
The Vole   71
The Vulture   73
The Walrus   74
The Wasp   76
The Water Buffalo   77
The Yeti   79
The Zorilla   80
The Zoo   80

The Alligator

The Alligator and the Crocodile
Look exactly the same from beneath,
But from the top you'll notice the difference,
In the eyes and the razor-sharp teeth.
Should you see either asleep on their backs,
Tanning their tums in the sun,
Don't turn them over to see which they are,
Just hazard a guess and then run.

The Antelope

Seldom is heard a discouraging word
Where the Deer and the Antelope play,
But when it is . . . it comes from Antelope,
As the Deer has few bad things to say.

Their complaints are usually aimed at the horns
Which protrude from the Antelope's head.
They may look quite fetching to you and to me,
But they'd much prefer antlers instead.

Though antlers are big and unsightly,
The Deer never feels a Baboon.
After all, who wants horns on the side of his head
When neither can knock out a tune.

So why are antlers so popular?
What is it that antlers do?
Well, apparently they're indispensable
When you're trying to get BBC 2.

The Armadillo

So hard was the shell of the poor Armadillo
That he longed to bed down on a feather-filled pillow.
He enquired of a Swan who swam on Lake Pawme,
'Donate your feathers and make a pillow for me!'
(*There is, of course, no such place as Lake Pawme,*
But isn't it a clever rhyme?)
Swan said she couldn't spare one single feather
If she was to live through the inclement weather.
'A few feathers for me won't make you go bald,'
The departing, cold Armadillo called.
'I'm sorry,' said the Swan, 'that's my final word.'
And I think it was, too . . . no more was heard.

On the trail of comfort went poor Armadillo,
His throbbing head yearning to rest on a pillow.
He tried a Duck, but the Duck said, 'You're joking!
Without feathers I won't be quacking, but croaking.'
Poor Armadillo was visibly shaken,
He thought Duck was his friend, but he was mistaken.
Said Duck, 'I'm sorry I can't help your head,
But why not stay and eat some of this bread?'
'No, if you can't spare a feather I'll go, Mister Duck.
You eat the bread and I hope it gets stuck!'

The Badger

Bill Brock was a badger
Who lived in Bluebell Wood.
He was a most unhappy Badger
But it must be understood
That the reason for his sorrow
Was a general lack of food,
Plus a great dislike of nightlife,
He thought Water Rats were crude.

You see, Bill had lost his mum
When he was just a mite,
He thought she must have lost her way
Because she strayed at night.
For Bill Brock thought it best to sleep
When daylight hours were done.
Besides, why quake beneath the moon
When the option was the sun?

The Spiders and the Beetles
Thought the Badger rather silly,
For whenever he approached, they yelled,
'Back to base lads, here comes Billy.'
The Spiders chanted cruel chants
At Billy the unmothered,
And the Beetles sang, 'She Loves You' —
(I'm surprised they weren't discovered).

No matter how hard Bill Brock tried
He couldn't find his dinner,
His footsteps became lighter,
His body became thinner.
Then one night a friendly fox
Came knocking at his door.
He told Bill that he had a plan
To fill his tummy more.

Fox said, 'Come out with me tonight
In your fur coat so black,
For Insects can't see in the dark
They haven't got the knack.
So if you creep up quietly
And scoop them on your tongue,
You'll eat a hearty supper
Before the moon has gone.'

Fox said to Badger, 'Can I come,
And my four cubs too, I beg?'
Badger caught a Spider
And they each chewed on a leg.
But Badger prefers to hunt alone
When the moonlight shines,
And he tends to lose his temper
So never cross the two white lines.

The Battery Hen

You expect little flattery when
You are born a Battery Hen.
With no feathers to keep you warm
Or chance to go pecking at corn,
You lay dozens and dozens of eggs
Until you go weak in the legs.
When the last one has fallen out,
Our chance of survival is nought.

Cluck, cluck, what terrible luck,
I should have been born a swan or a duck.
I feel of inferior class,
And laying eggs is a pain in the neck.

I'm afraid of foxes and guns.
I shiver 'til I get the runs.
When I reach the end of the line
I'm dressed in parsley and thyme.
If I lived my life all over again,
I'd rather be a free-range hen.
I'm in such a quandary, it's true.
I don't really know what to do.

You expect little flattery when
You are born a Battery Hen.
I've had hundreds of kids to date,
But they've all ended up on a plate.
To raise them all I've toiled,
But they end up scrambled and boiled.
Then, when I can't lay any more eggs,
Someone will chew off my legs.

Cluck, cluck, what terrible luck,
I should have been born a Swan or a Duck.
But I'm only a Battery Hen
Laying over and over again.

The Bear

A most inquisitive Polar Bear
Asked ('cause he wanted to know),
'As other Bears seem to be black or dark brown,
How comes I'm as white as the snow?'

A Grizzly Bear from the Rockies
(A most unapproachable beast)
Replied, 'Brown or white, so long as you fight,
I don't really mind in the least.'

'Who cares if you're white or red and green stripes,
Or blue with a big yellow spot.
Us brown ones, of course, are quite normal,
But we don't mind you lot who are not.'

So Polar Bear went to the Wise Owl,
'Mr Wise Owl, why am I white?
I think I look most unattractive.'
The Owl said, 'I think you're quite right.'

'I'll tell you what,' replied the Owl,
'Your question has me well beat.
I don't really see why animals
Should appear as though draped in a sheet.'

'That's it,' cried Bear, 'that's the reason!
That explains why my body is white.
I can creep up behind the grizzlies
And give them a horrible fright.

'When they turn around they'll think I'm a ghost.
Ooo, wouldn't that be funny?
They'll run and hide in the countryside,
Then I can steal all their honey.'

So he put his plan into action,
He went out the following night.
Up to the Bear . . .
He turned . . .
'Who's there?'
Then he saw the frightening sight.

'It's a ghost! Well shiver me timbers!'
(And some say his timbers shivered.)
He leaned on a tree where the ghost couldn't see,
The squirrels fell out as he quivered.

So that's why a Polar Bear's fur is white,
It's to frighten the Grizzly Bears.
And as Polar Bear is a big beast himself,
He's the only creature that dares.

The Boar

Barnaby Boar was a terrible bore,
His neighbours dreaded his stories.
Out for the count all creatures would flake,
Only the Crocodile stayed awake,
Which for Barnaby Boar was a dreadful mistake.
For when Crocodile let out a yawn,
Barnaby wished he'd never been born.
Croc's teeth were as sharp as a saw,
Now Barnaby Boar is no more.

The Canary

I shouldn't be down this mine at all,
A Canary should be in the sky.
All the miners glance at me
And hope that I won't die.
Because if I do they're in trouble . . .
Come to think of it so am I,
But I have to say it's the only way
I'll ever get up in the sky.

It isn't exactly wonderful
To be sitting down here for hours.
It's so hard to gauge the gilded cage
Or tropical scents and flowers.
All I get is dust on my beak
And grubby black marks on my wings.
When you feel so crude you are not in the mood
To wobble your beak and sing.

Now everybody has a dream,
And my dream is . . . one day,
They'll bring me out of this coal mine
And they'll let me fly away.
I'd laze in trees for the rest of my life
And sing 'til my throat was sore,
And I'll tell thee, they shan't see me
Down in the coal mine any more.

I'm a saddened, yellow Canary,
I should be up in the sky.
Why am I two miles down?
I should be two miles high.
I never flap my wings around,
All I get is cramp.
I've no idea where I am
Because they won't even give me a lamp.

The Cat

I

Long John Tabby was a Pussy Cat
And he worked in a factory.
Four-legged Cats caught flea-infested Rats,
But of legs Tabby only had three.
Yes, a three-legged Pussy was Tabby,
And in fairness he did what he could.
He thought he faced the dole
Until a kind-hearted soul
Made Tabby a new leg out of wood.
Clonk, clonk, clonk, he hit the Rats upon the head.
Clonk, clonk, clonk, he thumped them 'til they bled.
Clump, clump, clump, went the Rats out of the door.
Since Tabby got a wooden leg
You don't see Rats any more.

He found it hard to walk at first,
It all seemed such a drag,
With his solitary leg beneath his head.
With just one side of toes he could never pick his nose,
So he picked someone else's nose instead.
One side of his whiskers were full of grime and dirt,
He found washing rather difficult,
(So much so that it hurt).
But now three-legged Tabby is doing mighty fine
With his three good legs and his made-to-measure pine.
Clonk, clonk, clonk, he gave the Rats a thump.
Bonk, bonk, bonk, their heads came up in bumps.
Clump, clump, clump, the Rats all trooped away.
For them the time that Tabby came
Was a most distressing day.

So Long John Tabby is a hero,
To the men of the factory floor.
He used to be depressed
But now he's full of zest,
As the Rats run away bruised and sore.
Long John Tabby is showered with milk and meat
As the other Cats watch jealously.
Now they jump on all the traps
In the hope that one leg snaps,
Because the four-legged Cats wish they only had three.
Clonk, clonk, clonk, he hammers on the floor.
Clonk, clonk, clonk, goes his made-to-measure paw.
Clump, clump, clump, jump the Pussys on the traps.
Long John Tabby is the envy of the Cats.

The Cheetah

Rita the Cheetah
Was rather fond of curry.
That's why she was so fast . . .
She was always in a hurry.

The Cricket

A whipper-snapping Cricket asked his mother,
'Mother, why am I a whipper-snapping Cricket?
I am nothing like a bat,
I am well aware of that,
And I look even less like a wicket.'

The understanding mother told her youngster,
'It's because we go leaping through the clover.
They that give us names
Think our only aim's
Trying to jump to bowl a maiden over.'

The Dingo

It is easy to make a slight blunder
When listing the creatures down under.
Most forget the doggy-like Dingo
Who barks in a 'watcha blue' lingo.
He's ignored like the insecure Wombat,
Whose claws are kept sharpened for combat.
There's more there than Kangaroos
And unhouse-trained didgiredoos,
Who indulge in prolonged inactivity
And who never survive in captivity.
Now, please send me your views
On how you spell didgiredoos.

The Dogfish

Dennis the Dogfish lived in the sea,
Always complaining was Dennis,
He thought other fish were a menace,
He had dreams of living in Venice,
Did unrealistic Dennis.

Dennis the Dogfish dined alone,
He thought eating Worms a disgrace,
And small Crabs he just couldn't face.
(He disliked their dislikeable taste.)
Dennis felt so much out of place.

Dennis the Dogfish wagged his tail,
'What I want is meat!
Meat would be a real treat!
Meat would be really neat!
Meat simply cannot be beat!'

Dennis the Dogfish went out for a run
Around his imaginary park,
Giving an imaginary bark,
When he came face to face with a shark,
Out eating fish for a lark.

'You can't eat me! I'm Dennis the Dog.
I was a puppy, not an egg.'
He then proceeded to sit up and beg,
Doing all doggy things except cocking his leg,
Good thinking by Dennis the square peg.

Dennis the Dogfish had done very well,
Completely outwitting the beast
Who fancied an afternoon feast.
'I wasn't scared in the least,'
Said Dennis, still in one piece.

Dennis the Dogfish sat mopping his brow,
Then back came the Shark once more.
'I'm sorry to be such a bore,
You said you're a Dog . . . I'm not sure.
You have fins where there should be a paw.'

Dennis the Dogfish trembled,
'Now look here Mister fat Fish.
I'm a Dogfish out chasing Catfish.
The Shark curled his tail and sat . . . swish.
Dennis the Dog was a Flatfish.

The Dolphin

Dolphin rides,
Graceful she glides,
How she longs to be free.
When the crowds have gone home
She swims round alone,
Remembering her days in the sea.

Miles away beneath blue skies,
The sea is deep, the sun is high.
A Dolphin calls but comes no reply,
If only he knew he'd follow.
Roll up, roll up, the show has begun,
She's doing her tricks for everyone.
She knows in her heart he will never come,
But thinks . . . maybe tomorrow.

Dolphin rides,
Graceful she glides,
How she longs to be home.
Her tears fall like rain,
Her heart tears in pain,
In urge of the tropical foam.

Out on the ocean, as evening falls,
All is calm as her lover calls.
Children laugh 'til they cry in the stalls,
He knows his friend's in danger.
Never fear, as years go by,
Who will care if we live or die.
We shall never hear the Dolphin cry,
To them there's no creature stranger.

Dolphin rides,
Graceful she glides,
How she longs to be free.
What can we do to make her dreams come true?
Return her, one day, to the sea.

The Donkey

A poor beast of burden is the Donkey,
And it has been since the days of early man.
They are stupid and stubborn, pathetic and slow,
Unable to do the things *we* can.

Yet I think such descriptions are wayward.
He's a friend that's been left out in the cold.
It was he who carried the Virgin Mary,
And the prospector searching for gold.

The Earwig

We are two little Earwigs
But we don't live in ears.
We live in an observatory
(We've resided here for years).
And the trouble we have caused with our scurrying about.
I dread to see the professors when they find us out.
Earwig-O, Earwig-O, every time we tumble,
The mountains shake,
The valleys quake,
The earth begins to rumble.
Every time we jump around the earth splits in two.
Just think if we were bigger all the damage we could do.

We are two little Earwigs,
Sitting on a graph.

We move the needle up and down
Because it makes us laugh.
The trouble we have caused,
I just wouldn't like to say.
There was an earthquake last night
And a hurricane today.
Earwig-O, Earwig-O, every time we tumble,
The mountains shake,
The valleys quake,
The earth begins to rumble.
Every time we jump around the earth splits in two.
Just think if we were Hippos all the damage we could do.

The Eel

Two little Eels
Were sitting in the river,
Discussing the big, bruising Conger,
When one, full of pride,
Stood up and cried,
'They look just like us
. . . only longer!'

The Elk

Ernest the Elk,
Loved Winifred Whelk,
But their love couldn't possibly be.
For Ernest the Elk lived on dry land,
Whereas Winifred lived in the sea.

The Elephants and the Great
Bun-Fighting Contest

'Twas the day of the bun-fighting contest,
From everywhere Elephants came.
Some brought their mums,
Others brought sons,
Some even brought their own special buns.
Some came for a bit of a grin,
Others came solely to win.

The contestants arrived with their Elephant trunks
Packed with bun-fighting attire.
Huge balaclavas and dungarees,
The biggest-sized wellingtons
Up to their knees.
Some just wore a big sweater,
But quite frankly, the more clothes the better.

The teams stood round about five yards apart,
In two lines like formation dancers.
Some buns were spiced.
Others were iced,
And there were souvenir buns, well overpriced.
The Africans had the first throw
And it went when the judges yelled 'Go!'

The first bun took to the air like a Bird
And flew at the Indian ranks.
It splattered and split,
The first direct hit,
Bang on the forehead, it hurt quite a bit.
The icing started to run
And the receiver picked up a bun.

Back on two legs the Elephant stretched,
And then a swing of the trunk.
Soggy like a marshmallow,
It walloped an African fellow,
And burst in a bright blaze of yellow.
With all the strength he mustered
He covered his rival in custard.

Then all hell let loose and buns filled the air,
Backwards and forwards they went.
The African team
Were covered in cream,
and currents . . . and custard . . . a colourful scene.
Their foe didn't look any better.
(As a matter of fact they looked wetter.)

Nellie threw next (not the famous one
Who said goodbye to the circus),
A good throw by Nellie,
Straight in the belly.
The winded Indian shook like a jelly.
So losing and reeling with worry,
He took trunkfuls and trunkfuls of curry.

Out it shot at a fair rate of knots,
Pebbling the Africans' grey skin.
They fired once, then twice,
Most unfair and not nice,
Then finished it off with a few rounds of rice.
The Africans took a quick breather.
(They didn't smell too good either.)

The judges called them back into line,
The Africans had it all planned.
Dozens of rocks,
Coconuts by the box,
A couple of trees and some concrete blocks.
They flung them and gave hearty trumps,
And their rivals were covered in bumps.

'Most unfair,' mumbled Jumbo Madras,
'That's not my idea of a laugh.'
His team mates retreated,
Distraught and defeated,
Claiming the African throwers had cheated.
(Which made the atmosphere bad,
Even though they certainly had.)

Now the Indian Elephants never throw buns,
Since that terrible day in the jungle.
They do clever jobs,
Like moving big logs
And pulling out Hippos stranded in bogs.
But since that bun-fight defeat,
Buns are bought purely to eat.

The Ferret

A Ferret's a type of Polecat
Which hunts Rabbits
(A rather strange role, that).
When Rabbits abound,
They dive underground,
Saying, 'Cor that's a rather deep hole that.'

The Fly

A little chap who liked gossip,
Said, 'I wish I were a fly on the wall.'
Then his best friend said,
'You're round the bend, Fred,
That's what you *are*, you mad fool!'

The Fox

He travels alone through the jewelled frost of dawn,
Such a long night, now heading for home.
He lifts his nose to test the air,
There's a fragrance of dead wood, damp earth and bracken.
A scent wafts by, offending his senses,
Horses, hounds and the sporting human.

The blow of a horn awakens the brand new day,
Joined by the faint sounds of baying and yapping.
All thoughts of home are swept from his mind,
For another slyer plan and another direction.
To run and keep running 'til his heart nearly bursts,
Keeping his distance from the pack.

The earth vibrates to the hoof of the horse,
Fox twists and turns through familiar shrubs.
Ears back flat, mouth gaping in fear,
The stench of hounds swells in the air around him.
Into a stream, dogs in confusion,
He crouches in reeds for a moment's respite.

Panting, exhausted, he slumps to the ground,
Eyes submit, stinging, legs too heavy to trot.
What of his mate and hungry cubs,
Worrying and whimpering at his late arrival?
Over the brow, against the horizon,
But he knows he must rise and stumble on.

The scent is wayward at the water's edge.
Huntsmen curse and whipcracks resound.
Embarrassed dogs head for home,
Outwitted and outrun by the hunted.
Fear drains from his body and it's home to the set.
Freedom today, but what of tomorrow?

The Gibbon

Stanley the Gibbon and his youngest son Bobby
Were bored so decided to start a new hobby.
'Let's guess the age of bananas,' Bob said.
Said Stanley, 'You're mad,' and smacked Bob round the head.
Young Bobby cried,
His dad, Stanley, sighed.
No ideas sprang to mind though both of them tried.

Two explorers passed by in khaki and helmet.
Stan fancied their jackets for use on his pelmet.
He carried the two men back to his room.
One said, 'Doctor Livingstone, I presume?'
Stan said, 'Doctor Livingstone? Who?'
'You.'
'No, I'm Stanley the Gibbon,' and he started to chew.

He was nibbling away though he should have known better,
When from one of the pockets fell an unposted letter.
He licked at the letter until it was damp,
Enquiring, 'What's this?'
Said one man, 'A stamp.'
A brand new hobby for Stanley and Bob,
'That was to my wife,' said the man with a sob.

Though the stamp was in shreds it was the first one collected,
And caused much more interest than first was expected.
Ten little pieces of tuppenny blue
Were shown to each animal wandering through.
Stan said to a Bat,
'Mr Bat, look at that!'
Bat said, 'I've a far rarer black one than that.'

Stanley the Gibbon had found a new hobby.
'But Bat started first,' said the most astute Bobby,
'Or he wouldn't have owned that rare penny black,'
(Which brought one more painful, undeserved smack).
The Bat came with swaps again and again,
Stanley the Gibbon was destined for fame.

The Giraffes and Gorillas Meet Again at the Second Jungle Cup Final

Every year, when the Jungle Cup Final takes place,
There's no Liverpools, nor Aston Villas.
There are graceful teams like Giraffes and the Swans
And the dirty teams like the Gorillas.

In the previous year, Giraffes took the cup,
Much to Gorillas' surprise.
And Giraffes and Gorillas were meeting again,
Having won all their previous ties.

Giraffes had knocked out the Elephants
And had no problem beating the Voles.
They expectedly hammered the Spiders
(And in the process scored thirty-nine goals).

But the Spiders did well to get where they did,
With a shock win against the Partridges.
Due to weak legs most stayed in their webs
With damaged knee-caps and cartilages.

So Giraffes really played Spiders' reserves,
And the thrashing was hardly surprising.
Eleven brave chaps played 'til they collapsed
And their injury list kept on rising.

Gorillas were dirty as usual,
Determined to take home the cup.
The first round Foxes left the ground in boxes
And the Ladybirds didn't turn up.

Their non-appearance was due, so they say,
To a strong lack of self-control.
They threatened to beat up Gorillas
If the furry beasts scored the first goal.

So they decided not to turn up at all,
Though a good excuse had to be made.
They said their houses were burning down
And they awaited the fire brigade.

So the final kicked off, like the year before,
With Gorillas on the attack.
A Gorilla bit off a poor Giraffe's head
And was booed for not giving it back.

'Although I'm headless I'll carry on,'
Said the most courageous Giraffe.
He looked in such pain as time and again,
He headed the ball with his scarf.

'That's it, I just can't stand any more,'
As he walked from the field with regret.
Then the ball hit the lad on the back of the neck
And ricocheted into the net.

The crowd went completely bananas,
The Gorillas, one down and so soon,
Were sick as proverbial Parrots.
(Giraffes were over the moon.)

Ten minutes gone and a corner
And Giraffes once again went so close.
But what a fine save by the keeper so brave,
Who then ate half the crossbar and post.

Then just on the stroke of half-time,
Johnny Giraffe scored another,
Gorillas demanded it be disallowed,
Or they'd eat up the referee's brother.

'I'm not open to bribes, the goal stands,'
Said the overworked ref tired and torrid.
Besides, he felt that was no big deal,
(He thought his brother was horrid).

It looked like Giraffes would take home the cup,
So convincing in stature and style.
Yet Gorillas were finding their rhythm,
(So they sang and danced for a while).

Giraffes were getting too big for their boots,
Which explained their terrible blisters.
Most wore the cheapest boots money could buy.
(Tarquin Giraffe wore his sister's.)

Yes, the ruffians were getting back in the game
And forcing Giraffes to play deeper.
They not only pulled the two goals back,
But also the arms off the keeper.

Two goals and a few names into the book,
The ref was playing it firm.
One Gorilla claimed to be Keegan,
Back-combing his fur like a perm.

As full time blew, the excitement grew,
They played extra time for the winner.
Giraffes' centre half had been nibbled all game
And he looked considerably thinner.

He dribbled down the left side of the field,
Due to his lack of front teeth.
He crossed the ball to his team-mates so tall,
Yes, he certainly gave it some beef.

Over it came like a rocket,
The defence and attackers jumped up.
The ball found the head of right winger Jed,
And Giraffes, once again, won the cup.

Giraffes claimed to be invincible,
Though Gorillas' boss had his doubts.
He said he thought at the end of the day,
They were there or thereabouts.

'It's application and attitude,
And whoever scored the most goals.
On the day it wasn't quite right,
I doubt if we'd beaten the Voles.'

'I've said it before and I'll say it again,
The next game is always the toughest.'
Giraffes simply said of all teams they'd met,
Gorillas were by far the roughest.

The Hedgehog

Why does a Hedgehog roll up in a ball?
Do you think he's astute?
Or is he a fool?
There seems no logical reason at all.
Unless he's afraid of banging his head
As he wakes for the Summer
But still feels half dead.

Maybe he prefers to roll than to walk.
Then he doesn't waste time
Having to talk.
If he fell in a lake he'd float like a cork.
Perhaps it's because he's covered with fleas.
If he rolls in a ball . . .
They don't make him sneeze.

The Horse

Henry Horse lived in Newmarket
Like many Horses do.
He made no pretences,
He was quick over fences.
He knew it . . .
And others did too.

He had won all the biggest races
Like the Derby and the Oaks.
Henry, quite cocky, said,
'Who needs a jockey?'
Which, though right,
Hurt the poor little blokes.

When it came to the National at Aintree,
Henry was heard to boast,
'A few quid on me,
You'll be laughing, you'll see.'
. . . And they laughed!
(He was first past the post.)

But the laughers' laughing was short lived,
For they didn't win any pence.
The stewards officially said,
'That Horse with the very big head,
Lost his rider at the first fence.'

Henry was fairly disgusted
(As were the people that backed him).
He made an appeal,
But alas, no deal.
His trainer was so cross
. . . He sacked him.

Henry Horse lived in Newmarket
Like many Horses do.
He made no pretences.
He was quick over fences.
He knew it . . .
And the others did too.

It wasn't enough to be quick,
Though be it a vital part.
He just couldn't be told
So Henry was sold
Now he pulls
A scrap metal cart.

No matter who or what you are,
Listen to others' advice.
Henry the Horse,
Dreams of running the course
Walking the streets
Isn't nice.

The Hippo and the Insect

Now Horace the Hippo was terribly fat,
So the insects around him were terribly flat.
Some had flat legs, some had flat noses,
Some had flat kneecaps and others flat toeses,
Yes, the damage that Horace could do was immense,
So the feeling amongst the insects was tense.

His legs were heavyweight, leathery stumps
And they covered the insects with bruises and bumps.
One insect said, 'It's completely absurd.'
Another said, 'Blimey, that's a big word.'
Then clompety clomp the vibrations came,
'Forget the big words, here's that Hippo again.'

One said to the other, 'We must try to survive,
And the best way I know is by staying alive.'
Off they scampered at full speed ahead,
Eight little legs and two little heads.
Clompety clomp the Hippo grew near,
And the eight little legs shivered with fear.

The bravest of the small pair turned around,
Wiped his forehead and stood his ground.
Up came the Hippo, a menacing sight,
And he saw the insect trembling with fright.
'Good morning,' the Hippopotamus said,
Insect replied, 'One more step and you're dead.'

He raised his fists to the gigantic lump
One landed on Horace's knee with a thump.
So Horace, never lacking in humour,
Fell to the ground with a make-believe tumour.
'Ouch,' he shouted with tears in his eyes,
'Why don't you pick on someone your own size.'

Horace fell down with his legs in the air.
Then the insect hit him again . . . most unfair.
Then thinking the Hippopotamus dead,
Counted his blessings and hastily fled.
He found his friend hiding under a stone,
And yelled, 'I've killed him . . . all on my own.'

So the two little insects retraced the trail,
Those two little insects pathetic and frail.
They reached the spot where the slaughter had been,
But the posthumous Hippo couldn't be seen.
Where on earth had the mighty beast gone,
And more to the point, would he be long.

Yes, where on earth had the mighty beast fled,
And how did he do it if he was stone dead?
The insects will never learn the true story
How Horace the Hippo died for their glory.
Hippo thinks of the insects with sorrow,
For they're going Elephant-shooting tomorrow.

The Iguana

A jaundiced Iguana
Looks suspiciously like a banana,
And the other strange thing about him
Is you slip when you tread on his skin.

The Jaguar

Jaguars are fast-moving Cats,
Yet not as fast as the Cheetahs,
Which is most surprising when you think,
Most have engines of over three litres.

The Jellyfish

The Jellyfish,
Is not a smelly Fish,
That much is quite apparent.
They don't have things
Like scales or fins,
In actual fact,
They're transparent.

Yet whenever Fish have parties
As birthday treats
For their fry.
They always invite the Jellyfish
And I can't think of one reason why.

The Kestrel

The home of a Kestrel
Is no longer ancestral,
They live in those high-rise flats.
Not nooks or crannies,
Like their grandads or grannies,
Nor in trees like Squirrels or Bats.

The Kingfisher

If you sit very still by a river or brook,
You may just be lucky,
But then, you may not.
For you need to be sharp the Kingfisher to spy,
As he dives for his breakfast,
Then heads for the sky.

Though proud as a king he is painfully shy
As he sits resplendent
In gold and bright blue.
His black, beady eyes watch the shimmering lake
For a rising fish . . .
Or a mayfly to take.

A flash of blue,
Then a quick splash of blue,
Is all the king shall grant you.
Then back to his branch like a bird on a wing,
Enjoying his supper . . .
Fit for a king.

The Limpet

Les Limpet lived under a boat,
And he travelled the seven seas.
Wherever the boat went, Les did too
. . . Australia, Asia, Timbuktoo.
He lived with his father and mother,
And his sister, and much younger brother.
Five little shells on a boat,
'Five beautiful shells' (and I quote).

Les held on as firm as he could
To the polyurethane wood.
For the one thing that frightened him
Was the fact that he just couldn't swim.
He had no arms at all and one solitary leg
Upon which was wedged a slipper.
(He'd had a slipper for his birthday and Christmas,
And had done since he was a nipper.)

His family had slippers for birthdays too,
So the gifts never held a surprise.
The only exciting difference
Was the colour and sometimes the size.
Then he came up with a great idea
And that Christmas he asked for a flipper.
At last he would swim, then Mum said to him,
'They only had eights so I bought you a slipper.'

The Lion and the Sea Lion

A Sea Lion and a Lion
Are completely different creatures.
They have entirely different temperaments
And entirely different features.

A Sea Lion says, 'Good morning,
Isn't it a wonderful day.'
But the Lion says nothing,
Just bites off your leg to stop you running away.

The Lion has long matted hair
Which would drive the Sea Lion barmy,
For he prefers a short back and sides
Like a chap in the air force or the army.

The scruffy one runs like a sprinter,
Yet the other's too clumsy to walk.
But the Sea Lion never need worry,
Because he floats like a cork.

And that's what makes Lion angry.
That's what aggravates him.
When a Grasshopper says, 'See that Lion,
Do you know he can't even swim.'

The Lizard

Lenny the Lizard went out in a blizzard,
The cold winter wind was a-blowing.
He never liked living in England,
Especially when it was snowing.
He changed colour to match his surroundings,
He'd been brown the previous night,
But due to the blizzard, Lenny the Lizard
Had changed to a most fetching white.

He longed to be back in the tropics,
With the sun belting down on his head . . .
Drinking an oasis's water-hole dry,
Until the sun turned him red.
He felt stupid looking like Snow White,
It made him feel grumpy and sneezy.
He tried to forget his appearance
(Which quite frankly wasn't that easy).

One day he was writing some postcards
To his sun-drenched friends in the south,
When along came an unfriendly Seagull,
Who popped Lizard into his mouth.
'What do you think you are doing?
Let me out!' demanded the Lizard.
(And to attract the Seagull's attention
He jumped up and down in his gizzard.)

'Be quiet, Mr Lizard,' said the Seagull,
'I'd like to make a suggestion.
But if you keep leaping about down there,
You'll give me acute indigestion.'
So Lenny sat down in the Seagull
And listened to what Bird had planned.
Then Lizard agreed to be flown at great speed
To a warm equatorial land.

So off went the lucky old Lizard,
Calming himself en route.
'I'm nervous, I think, I must have a drink.'
He soon was as drunk as a newt.
They ground to a halt in the desert
Where the Bird let his passenger out.
'I must be in the Sahara.'
(Then a Camel trod on his snout.)

So Lenny the Lizard sat contented,
Merging with the colour of the sand.
An Arab said, 'Where are you from, Mr Lizard?'
But Len was English and he didn't understand.
Seagull returned from whence he came
Leaving young Leonard alone.
Should you go searching for him or his friends,
They'll be sleeping under a stone.

The Mole

There once lived a Mole,
A droll Mole,
Who tunnelled and wriggled
But seldom giggled.
He toiled through the safety of night
And seldom played the fool.
He couldn't see why he needed to laugh
(He couldn't see nothing at all).

Then one bright day,
Whilst dreaming away,
Sighing and snoring,
Twitching and clawing.
So began the very first Mole hill,
As soil spouted out like a fountain.
The more Mole threw the more the hill grew,
Until it stood as high as a mountain.

Tons of soil shot into the air.
Through grey rainclouds
And into beyond.
Ice formed on top and it glistened,
As though stroked by a fairy's wand.

He dug more and more
With both right and left claw.
Hundreds and hundreds of feet,
Steep, yet incredibly neat.
It disappeared deep into space,
With an ambitious Mole on the face.
Now fields seem to get a crop of them,
But you can't make mountains out of them.

The Money Spider

A most disconsolate Money Spider
Looked very, very strange.
He was born in the shape of a fifty-pence piece
And the years hadn't brought on much change.
Then a Hippo not checking his bearings,
Trod straight on the poor fellow's head.
He may have resembled a fifty-pence piece,
But now he looks like a pound note instead.

The Monkey

Marvin the miserable Monkey
Saw the world from a strange point of view.
He lived in the trees where the Bats lived
And did what all good bats do do*.
He hung upside down in the branches
With the blood rushing straight to his head.
He had pins and needles in his tail
And his face was a brilliant red.

Every night as the darkness took over,
The Bats all flew from their bed.
Once, Marvin tried to do just the same
And fell to the ground on his head . . . dead!
There's a moral to a story like this one,
Even if Monkey's got guts,
He shouldn't go hanging in trees upside down,
He'd be better off breaking up nuts.

So that's where the old proverb comes from –
'To make hay while the sun shines.'
Or was it, 'Too many cooks spoil the broth,'
Or 'A stitch in time saves nine.'
Or perhaps it was, 'Every dog has its day,'
Yes, that's right, I think it was that.
Well, whatever it was it had little to do
With an upside down Monkey or Bat.

*An extinct Mauritian bird, for your reference.

The Letter N

Did you know an N is a cockney chicken?

The Nutria

Nutrias and Beavers
Are more or less the same.
It seems the only difference
Is the spelling of the name.
If you ask both creatures
If they're Nutrias or Beavers;
I doubt if they could help you.
(And I doubt if I could either!)

The Octopus

Fish big and small fear the Octopus
Though not for the reasons you think.
For if they're attacked by harpoons or the like
The fishes get covered in ink.
Which would be all right if they used it,
But the poor things don't have the knowledge.
It's hard enough getting them going to school,
Let alone Tentacle College.
Which is all very well for the Octopus.
Soon it will all be history.
No more ink, only silicon chips,
And the more chips the less fish there'll be.
Now, the only fish you find in schools
Are intelligent Dolphins and Whales,
But there's millions of others down there in the deep

Who don't know their heads from their tails.
It's a problem that haunts the Conger Eels,
Whose ends are exactly the same.
This means at partytime postman's knock
The Eels get banned from the game.
The Herring confirm it's a good job, too,
They never kiss Eels in the dark.
But the sad thing as regards the Congers
Is neither end bothers the Shark.
Anyway, I digress.

Poor Octopus isn't asked anywhere,
Just because he looks a bit strange.
Which is sad 'cause I'm sure if he had a choice
He'd welcome a bodily change.
One day, against all expectations,
A fancy dress party was planned.
Somebody sent him an invite
Which the others could not understand.
'Why him?' said the Dab to the Mackerel,
'He's not in any good books.
The only way I'd like to see him there
Is dragged head first by the cooks.'
Meanwhile, back at home in his shipwreck,
Octopus planned his disguise.
'Who could I be?' he asked himself,
'What would give me the first prize?
I could paint myself as black as the night,
Find a female and sit down beside her.
She could be Little Miss Muffett
And I could be a big spider.
No, that wouldn't give me the first prize,
It's been done far too many times.'
(I would like to ask at this juncture
How Octopus knew nursery rhymes?)
Do you know what he finally went as?
Do you know what he finally did?
He wore a badge of the Queen on each side of his head
. . . And went as a couple of Squid.

The Ostrich

Something so hard to understand
Is why Ostriches such as I,
Bury our heads and our necks in the sand.
It must be said we must be dense,
For we'd use a spade if we had any sense.
All that sand can get stuck in your eye,
Which stops tears falling out when you cry.

We never hear our predators come,
We jump when they hit us hard on the . . . head.
Should you see one as I,
With its head in the sand,
Don't laugh too loud,
We just don't understand.

Amanda the Panda

Amanda the Panda,
Lived in Uganda,
And the fact she'd never mated
Was Amanda's big regret.
The problem of Amanda's?
Nearly all the other Pandas
Were Chinese,
And those that weren't
Lived somewhere in Tibet.

The Pigeon

Herman, he went to Germany,
To France and Holland and Spain.
He was supposed to fly to Swindon
And then fly home again.
His navigational qualities were never up to much.
He left speaking pidgin English
And came back speaking Dutch.

Herman, he went to Germany
Like Hurricanes did in the war.
En route he dropped more deposits
Than the Liberals in 'seventy-four.
Yes Herman the Homing Pigeon
Found it so hard to come home.
But he never thought much of Swindon
So he flapped off for nine months to Rome.

Meanwhile back in Wiltshire
Others had found their way home,
But Arnold, poor bloke, was a standing joke
As Herman continued . . . alone.
What had got into his Pigeon?
Where on earth could he be?
Herman was having a grand old time,
For once in his life he was free.

He passed over country and ocean,
Higher and higher he flew.
He was flapping his wings like a goodun',
Nine months well overdue.
His master was so disappointed
That Herman had never checked in.
So upon his return he was anxious to learn
Exactly where Herman had been.

'What time do you call this?' asked Arnold.
'About twenty past two,' said the stray.
'I'd have been home before had I not been caught
In the one-way streets of Bombay.'
'Have you a true explanation
Before I send you to bed?'
Said Herman, 'Only one thing springs to my mind,'
And it landed on poor Arnold's head.

Yes Herman, he went to Germany,
To France and Holland and Spain.
He was supposed to fly to Swindon
And then fly home again.
His navigational qualities were never up to much.
He left speaking pidgin English
And came back speaking Dutch.

The Piranha

A rather short-sighted Piranha
Each lunchtime ate a banana.
Then one day he ate four fingers and a thumb,
Not intentionally you understand.
It's hard for Piranhas to find 'nanas
And the fingers were the closest thing to hand.

The Prairie Dog

I don't think a Prairie Dog
Is a particularly hairy Dog.
Apart from its name being Prairie Dog
It's as much like a Dog as a Cow or a Frog.
It's only its bark-like call,
Which makes it Dog-like at all.
It doesn't live in a kennel
Like a Corgi or a Red Setter,
But in a burrow beneath the ground,
Where it reckons the heating is better.

It resembles a common old Squirrel
Despite its unsuitable name.
It don't even live on the prairies
So I wonder from where the name came.
Perhaps it likes chewing raw meat off bones
Or lying curled up by the fire,
But whoever said the Prairie Dog
Was like any other hairy Dog
Was a bit of a dog-gone liar.

The Quail

A Quail once fancied learning to sail,
He thought it would be rather pleasant,
Though I think it a case of oneupmanship
Over the strutting, big-headed Pheasant.

For everything the little Quail did,
The Pheasant did quicker and better.
So Quail knew if his feathers got wet,
Pheasant's would get even wetter.

So off he went to the river,
To a Swan who hired himself out
As a beginner's, unsinkable dinghy . . .
Quail started splashing about.

He was rather enjoying the lesson
When Pheasant appeared on the bank.
He waded in with a sarcastic grin,
But most unexpectedly sank.

He kicked and he splashed in the shallows,
Screaming as loud as he could,
But the river was only four inches deep
(As he'd have found out if he'd stood).

Naughty Quail laughed his head off,
Pheasant glowed embarassing red.
So there stood a bright-coloured Pheasant
And a Quail without any head.

That's why you seldom see Pheasants
Residing by river and stream.
'If we'd been expected to swim,' one said.
'We'd have been a gudgeon or bream.'

As for the Quail without any head,
It was only a play on words.
But it has to be said, without or with head,
The Quail is a rather odd bird.

The Rabbit

Well it's sad but true to say
I've really gone off my Rabbit.
Ever since reading *Watership Down*
He's made posing quite a habit.
He struts around importantly,
Hardly frightened any more,
And he's refusing to eat carrots,
Saying they make his eyesight poor.
What's more he won't stay in at nights,
He goes out chasing Foxes.
He used to eat his droppings,
Now he wraps them up in boxes.
Apparently when he's famous
They'll fetch a tidy sum.
My, my, Richard Adams,
If you knew what you had done.

He's even changed his name
From Floppy Ears to Seamus,
He says it's more in keeping
With the middle class and famous.
He's got a mirror and a hairbrush
Plus a TV for his cage,
And a new ambition . . .
To play Hamlet on the stage.
Dear Richard Adams,
Whatever have you done?
Before you wrote that wretched book
We used to have such fun.
Yes it's sad but true to say
I've really gone off my Rabbit.
Ever since reading *Watership Down*
He's made posing quite a habit.

The Reindeer

Ray Reindeer was most unreliable,
For he could never remember the date.
He delivered presents as good as the next,
But nine times out of ten they were late.

His nose wasn't shiny like Rudolph's
And he never led any sleigh pack.
If he had they'd have set off from Lapland
And forgotten to ever come back.

Now it was a dark and parky morning,
The snow was inches deep.
Santa wasn't too happy,
(His wellingtons had a leak).

He was still hung over from a stag do,
His nose was oh so bright.
He told poor Ray, 'This is your lucky day,
You're on your own tonight.'

So with a list of the addresses,
And a Father Christmas cap,
Off Ray shot and clean forgot
His compass and his map.

It was Christmas Eve in Lapland
(and in Great Britain too),
Mums and dads were restless,
Their toys were well overdue.

Excited children waited
For footsteps on the roof,
But forgetful Ray was miles away
(They never heard one hoof).

Over Wigan, France then Egypt,
The forgetful Reindeer flew.
He knew he was going somewhere,
But where? He hadn't a clue.

In his sack the dolls and soldiers
Were tired and depressed.
They longed to stop on a chimney top
In Wigan . . . like the rest.

Where is he Father Christmas?
Said Santa, 'I don't know.
The last I heard he was stacking
With the jets above Heathrow.'

On July the fourth he landed
Dejected and alone.
For six months he'd been missing.
For six months he had flown.

He came down in Australia
At an outback children's home.
He said, 'I'd have told you I'd be late,
But I couldn't find a phone.

'Happy Christmas everybody,
There are presents for all of you here.'
Such pleasure for children who thought
Christmas came but once a year.

The Robin

A Robin has a red breast.
'But why?' you may enquire.
Perhaps poor Robin feels the cold
And sits too near the fire.

For he calls in drab December
While others soak the sun.
He sits on every Christmas card
And stays 'til winter's done.

A Robin has a red breast
For a very simple reason;
He still looks rather sun-tanned
Despite the festive season.

So when Swallows are swooping
And others are returning,
They may look brown and healthy
But Robin glows as though he's burning.

For his loyalty and bravery
Mother Nature paints his breast.
Every Bird is pretty
But the Robin is the best.

The Skunk

There once was a skunk
Who got terribly drunk.
He couldn't see straight,
So he attempted to mate
With a sack of manure
Which stank like a sewer.
Now the moral is, if you're a Skunk,
Have fun but don't get blind drunk.

The Slug

Swinbourne Slug was exhausted,
So off he went to a sauna.
He started to doze,
The temperature rose,
Now Swinbourne's a pool in the corner.

Two Snakes

Viper Vic was a clever old stick,
He could whip through his sums like an adder.
He lost his poor Mum when she bit her tongue,
He felt sad . . . but his Mother felt sadder.
Vic was alone, he started to roam,
Then he met a Boa-Constrictor.
She thought he was lush and developed a crush
(Which meant time to slide off for Victor).

Viper Vic met Mamba Mick,
He thought of him as his best buddy,
And Mick, who was nearly two inches thick,
Lived where the jungle was muddy.
Mick's marriage to the much admired Mo,
Was just battle after pitched battle.
For she'd presented Mick, whose temper was quick,
With a newly born snake with a rattle.

While the baby snake gurgled and rattled away
Mick puffed with rage (like they do).
He said, 'Maureen, that youngster looks nothing like me
And it's not a *great* likeness of you.'
'Don't be so silly,' his wife replied,
'He's got your eyes and your nose.
He may look like a Rattlesnake now, my dear,
But he'll look more like you when he grows.'

'I'm not hanging around that long,' said Mick,
'You've been deceitful to me.
Do you think I don't know the difference between
A Rattler and Mamba like me?

'No, me and my new friend Victor
Whom I met in the mud yesterday
Are going to slither all round the world
And we'll make lots of friends on the way.'
So off went Vic and the Mamba,
Sliding and feeding on Mice.
(Victor tried eating a Skunk as well
But it didn't taste very nice.)

Although Victor and Michael's progress was slow
(About fifty yards every day),
They enjoyed each other's company
Both in serious moments and play.
But if you think this story ends happily
I'm afraid it doesn't my friend,
For Victor tried mugging a Mongoose
And met a predictable end.

The Squirrel

Cyril Squirrel lived in a big oak tree
At the top of a fine oak staircase.
Up he scampered when danger grew near,
Then down he cascaded when all was clear.
Such a popular chap was Cyril,
The scampering, cascading Squirrel.

Now Cyril, although remarkably slight,
Had a heart of oak like the staircase.
He defeated creatures ten times his own size.
He said he'd killed Tigers (Cyril told lies!).
An heroic deed for good measure
Brought the other creatures such pleasure.

One night he related the story
Of Owls in the overhead airspace,
Swooping and dining on terrified Mice,
They needed to go regardless of price.
It was Cyril who planned the demise
Of the rulers of midnight skies.

It must have been eleven-fifteen,
Or perhaps twenty-five-past eleven.
The Fieldmice and Voles appeared from holes
Pushed to the surface by constructing Moles.
The Owls rubbed their wings and giggled
As the suppers beneath them wriggled.

Cyril Squirrel lay in wait that night,
At the top of the fine oak staircase.
As the Owls began their Mouse-spotting,
Cyril began his Owl-squatting.
From the branches high in the trees,
Acorns came down like swarms of Bees.

'Ouch,' the Owls hooted disconsolately,
As acorns spilled from the staircase.
'We'll get you Cyril Squirrel for that,'
Then they dive-bombed the branch where Cyril sat.
But Cyril put *them* through their paces,
Which is why Owls have pushed-in faces.

The Tiger
(The Sabre-Toothless Tiger)

A Sabre-Toothless Tiger
Feels down upon his luck.
He can't bite lumps off his enemy,
(But *can* give a nasty suck).

The Turbot

Herbert the Turbot was terribly flat.
The other fish said, 'What in heaven's name's that?
It can't be a kite, it hasn't got strings.
It can't be a fish, it hasn't got fins.'
But Herbert replied, 'Yes I am,'
And he buried his head in the sand.

Herbert said, 'Years ago and it's true,
Turbots were bigger than people like you.
Ten feet tall some were known,
A hundred pounds of muscle and bone.
Then things went tragically wrong.'
So the other fish burst into song;

'A hundred pounds and ten feet tall?
Herbert the Turbot's a silly old fool.
He's lost the sense that he had,
Herbert the Turbot is mad.'

'Yes once we were mighty,' the Turbot said,
'Til a Whale came and sat on grandad's head.
"Ouch!" said grandad and so did the Whale,
Saying "What have I sat on now?"
Grandad boldly replied, "You've sat on me!"
Then he died.'

'Herbert the Turbot's a silly old fool,
You can't believe a story so tall.
He's lost the sense that he had,
Herbert the Turbot is mad.'

None of the fish believed what he said.
They chuckled and laughed as they passed overhead.
A shadow appeared . . . a trawlerman's net,
Swallowed up every fish it met.
But Herbert the Turbot being so flat
The net passed over where he sat.
Herbert the Turbot was saved,
Unlike the badly behaved.

Herbert we think the world of you.
Herbert we know your stories are true,
But the flatfish said, 'Too late,
Good luck at Billingsgate.'

'A hundred pounds and ten feet tall?
Herbert the Turbot's a silly old fool.
He's lost the sense that he had.
Herbert the Turbot is mad.'

Mr Turtle

He travelled around like a gipsy man,
His home on his back like a caravan.
He told me of the places he'd been,
The miles he had travelled,
The things he had seen.
Some of his travellers' tales were absurd,
But I never disputed his wisdom or word.
He made us smile and then cry
With stories as tall as the sky.

Hey Mr Turtle, what a nice fella,
Hey Mr Turtle, what a story-teller,
Like a wizard he cast a spell,
Then disappeared in his shell.

He travelled the oceans from France to Spain,
Once round the world then once round again.
Seeing rivers in faraway lands,
Reliving it all with maps in the sand.
Listeners came with their children and wives
As the magical stories brought joy to their lives.
He may not have been anywhere,
But nobody questioned or cared.

Hey Mr Turtle, what a nice fella,
Hey Mr Turtle, what a story-teller,
Like a wizard he cast a spell,
Then disappeared in his shell.

Tell us a story before you go,
Is it really that cold where the icebergs flow?
The gypsy blood is beginning to boil,
He must take his home to a distant soil,
He waves goodbye with a tear in his eye,
We never ask where and we never ask why.
We accept it's a traveller's way
He hasn't the time to stay.

Hey Mr Turtle, what a nice fella,
Hey Mr Turtle, what a story-teller,
Like a wizard he cast a spell,
Then disappeared in his shell.

The Vole

There once was a Vole who lived in a hole
By the banks of a fast-running stream.
His floor was dirty, all covered in mud
And his furniture needed a clean.
A clean, yes that's all it required,
But Vole was always too busy and tired.

It was oh such a mess but Vole couldn't care less,
So long as he had room to snooze.
Others tried matching his mayhem
But more often than not they would lose.
For even the scruffy old Rats,
Had curtains, carpets and mats.

But things were to change quite considerably
When Vole fell in love with a Shrew.
'Why not come round for some breadcrumbs?'
But madam replied, 'No thank you.'
'I've heard of your scruffy old place
And quite frankly it sounds a disgrace.

'Ask me again when you've tidied it up,'
Then she turned around and was gone.
Vole scampered as fast as his legs allowed
And he polished his house 'til it shone.
Yes he polished until he drew blood,
And he could see his face in the mud.

Off he went to relocate Shrew
Who alas was nowhere to be seen.
He looked behind every twig so small
And every leaf so green.
'Good morning, little Vole,'
(It was Maurice the neighbourly Mole).

'Ah, Mister Mole,' said the trembling Vole,
'Have you seen my amorous Shrew?'
Mole said, 'Put it on and let me see,'
Said Vole, 'My *Shrew* not my *shoe*.'
'That hole was where she used to be
But now she's up in that tree.'

'Up in the tree . . . what do you mean?'
Pleaded the weeping Vole.
'She ran away with Tawny Owl
Now she lives in that tree, not that hole.'
Vole said, 'This cannot be true,
I was going to marry that Shrew.'

'I bet she wasn't too willing
To go swanning off with some Owl.
It seems about as unlikely
As me going out with a Cow.
No, that Owl had nasty ideas.'
Then the little Vole broke down in tears.

He wandered home despondently,
Clenching his paws in frustration.
He was so mad at what the bad Owl had done
He attacked a passing Alsatian.
The Owl had eaten his Shrew
And the Vole met his maker too.

The Vulture

The trouble with a Vulture
Is he ain't got no culture.
He don't chew his meat . . . he tears it.
I don't know how his victims bare it.
When a poor deer comes a cropper
It hopes it gets ate proper,
But the idea's out of the question,
But listen,
Here's a good suggestion . . .

Why don't a Vulture,
And this is my suggestion,
Why don't a Vulture
Ever get no indigestion?
For if it ate its food up good
Then all'd be understood,
But here,
It's got manners like a pig,
Even if the meat is big.

Yeah that's the trouble with a Vulture,
It's got no blooming culture.
So if you see one in the sky
Do your utmost not to die.
I know he'll miss out on a peck,
But if you're still here what the heck.

The Walrus

Walrus looked on lovingly;
'I am a Clam,
That's what I am.'
The words set his heart a-fluttering,
'I am a Clam,
Will you be my man?'
And he fell for the little shell's muttering.

Walrus replied to the cry from the heart;
'Marry a Clam?
I don't think I can.
I'm s.s.sorry,' said Walrus (stuttering),
'It's not on at all,
I'm big and you're s.s.small,'
Ignoring the Clam's eyelids fluttering.

She wouldn't take no for an answer;
'Please marry me!
It'll be fine, you'll see.
My dear I love you something chronic.'
But Walrus replied,
'I can't make you my bride.'
Our relationship must be platonic.

Clam was alone in this world.
'You've eaten my brother,
And sister and mother.
And if our love cannot be
Then continue your feast,
You big, ugly beast.
You might as well gobble up me.'

Walrus accepted the challenge,
But he just couldn't do it.
It was not on, he knew it.
He wasn't that sort of a mammal.
Clam ran away,
And I hear yesterday,
She got engaged to a Camel.

The Wasp

There once was a Wasp called Wally,
Who fancied another called Win.
He asked her out to the pictures.
She accepted . . . and they saw 'The Sting'.

They sat in the back row together,
Embracing with legs wrapped in legs.
'One day I'm going to get married,' said Win,
'And have dozens and dozens of eggs.'

'Good Golly,' said Wally, 'I'd like that too.
I like eggs as much as you do.
Poached or scrambled, I don't really mind,
But not raw, they're tricky to chew.'

Win was staggered. She brushed him aside.
Wally cried, 'What have I said?
Kiss me, Win!' . . . But she turned to 'The Sting'
And watched Robert Redford instead.

She felt his breath in her left ear.
His heart had increased its ticking.
She slapped his legs . . . 'If you want to eat eggs,
I suggest you marry a Chicken.'

Wally buzzed out of the back row
At twenty-five minutes past ten.
Out of spite he sped at full flight,
And at midnight he married a Hen.

The Water Buffalo

Walter Buffalo the Water Buffalo
Led a dual purpose life.
A.M. with master he pulled a great plough
And P.M. he helped master's wife.

He preferred the P.M. to A.M.,
He could do what she asked with great ease.
But A.M. for him was dreary and dim
As he trudged in mud up to his knees.

When the bell went at noon, Walter was pleased,
He could take the weight off his corns.
For the grateful beast knew, all she could do
Was hang laundry the length of his horns.

Other beasts said, 'We won't be seen dead
With vests and pants in our eye.
We only use horns for punch-ups,
Not for letting underwear dry.'

But Walter Buffalo stuck to his task,
A little embarrassed of course.
He became the first clothes-Buffalo,
As opposed to the common clothes-Horse.

The Yeti

Do you know the subtle difference
Between a Mongoose and a Yeti?
Well, the Yeti eats snowballs like ice-cream,
While the Mongoose eats Snakes like spaghetti.

The Zorilla

The Zorilla sounds like a Gorilla,
Of that I'm sure you're aware,
But the Zorilla's body is black and white stripes
And Gorillas are covered in hair.
One punch from the Gorilla
And you're out for a rather long doze.
One whiff of the smelly Zorilla
Sends you running off holding your nose.

Now if I could choose my destiny,
Which of these ways would I go?
I'd prefer the Z to the G-type . . .
Though on second thoughts . . . I don't know.
The Zorilla's smell is so awful,
And it wafted to me when it shook.
My pen has started wilting,
So this is the end of the book.

The Zoo

Another selection has drawn to a close.
I hope you like the creatures I chose.
Now you know what these animals do,
Why not see them down at the Zoo?
They get rather bored sitting in cages,
So why not read them a few of these pages.
It's certain to raise a chuckle or two,
And you will be a friend of theirs too.